Building
Relati...

Bella

The Empathy Adventure

Grades 1-5

written by
Sandy Ragona

illustrated by
Brian Caleb Dumm

youth light inc.

© 2012 by YouthLight, Inc.
Chapin, SC 29036

Illustrations and Cover Design by Brian Caleb Dumm
Design and Layout by Diane Florence
Project Editing by Susan Bowman

ISBN: 9781598501193

Library of Congress Number
2012936628

10 9 8 7 6 5 4 3 2 1
Printed in the United States

Dedication

I dedicate this book to Bella, my granddaughter, the love of my life.

This book is also dedicated to our children who understand the feelings of others. Each day that our children reach out to comfort a classmate or to celebrate in the joy of a happy occasion, they are showing empathy. They know that empathy is the foundation of healthy relationships.

This book is also dedicated to educators who teach students that caring for others is vital to developing sound character. The educator who models empathy and values the role of reaching out to others is helping the next generation to become more civil and just. As we work to stop bullying, hate, and disrespect, let us not forget that to become a more just nation we must show each other empathy and a willingness to reach out.

Show you care.

Acknowledgements

I would like to thank Youthlight, Inc. for their encouragement and support from the inception to the completion of this book.

To Brian Dumm, thank you for another opportunity to work with you. You have talent, creative eye, and expertise to make words on a page come alive with art.

I owe a big thank you to my students at J.F. Kennedy School in Dubuque, Iowa. To Mrs. Anderson and her third grade students, thank you for helping me develop Bella's adventure with your ideas and constructive comments. You gave me the perspective of seeing the book through the eyes of a child.

To my other kindergarten through fifth graders, all 549 of you, thanks for your feedback as the storyline was completed.

Most importantly, I would like to thank my husband, Andy, for his support and encouragement with many of my ideas. He is always at my side.

I thank my son and daughter-in-law, Joe and Mindy, for giving me a beautiful granddaughter, Bella. At eighteen months, she shows empathy with hugs, kisses and love.

If you want to be popular, you can't be mean to others. Bella: The Empathy Adventure taught me to be nicer. Now I know that when someone gets hurt, I will help them up instead of walking past them. Now I realize, if someone is having trouble understanding the game, I will explain it to them. Empathy taught me how to be nicer.

—Jim, Kennedy third grade student

Introduction

Bella: The Empathy Adventure is a book that is evidence based. This book is effective in teaching elementary students that empathy is a foundation to healthy relationships. The three steps outlined in the story give students the knowledge to know what empathy is and what to say and do to show others empathy in their daily interactions.

The findings concluded:

- 70% of 8-11 year olds didn't know what empathy is or what to say or do.
- The need to teach that understanding the feelings of others builds friendships.
- Modeling social skills provided students with ways to show empathy.

In informal pretests before reading the book, third through fifth graders, (211 students) were asked:
- What is empathy? What would you say or do to show empathy?

After listening to a reading of the book, ***Bella: The Empathy Adventure***, and role playing empathy skills, students in third through fifth grade were post tested. They were asked to define empathy and to describe words and actions that show empathy.

	Pretest results	Posttest results
Third grade:	28%	88%
Fourth grade:	37%	98%
Fifth grade:	39%	96%

The results indicated that students learned ways to respond to the feelings of others. They felt empathy towards their peers in all situations and related to them with pro-social behavior.

Bella

The Empathy Adventure

Bella loved to travel and learn new things. She read many books and talked to several people about what empathy means. She asked many times about why empathy is so popular, but never received an answer from anyone. So one day, Bella set out on a journey to find the answer.

She heard that to be liked by people you have to show empathy. Bella dreamt about her trip and what she would learn along the way. There was so much to experience that Bella was excited to start the journey that would change her life. She grabbed her coat and hat and picked up her backpack. Her adventure was just beginning.

Bella started walking and found that the road was hilly and steep. She climbed each hill with more excitement wondering what she would find along the way. She started running, gaining speed as she approached a valley of flowers.

Off in the distance, she saw a squirrel that was sitting in a field of purple clover. Bella walked to meet her.

Sofia Squirrel said, "I have been waiting for you.
Please sit down in the grass and learn about empathy.
I can answer your questions and I will help you
to understand."

Sofia explained, "Empathy is the ability to understand what others feel and to express that in a caring way. It is the social emotion that connects all of us." "For example, if I was crying because I didn't have anyone to play with, you would understand my sadness and feel my loneliness," Sofia exclaimed.

Bella looked excited. "I get it," she said. "I need to pay more attention to how others feel. When I see someone feeling sad, I need to feel their sadness too." Sofia Squirrel gave Bella a bright yellow star with the words: **understand feelings** across the middle of the star. "Place this in your backpack to remind you to understand other's feelings. Empathy is important in friendships," she noted.

Sofia and Bella walked through the purple clover field and entered the forest. The trees were tall and the sunlight grew dimmer. They found a path between the trees and started to walk down the trail together.

The path stopped in front of field of yellow daisies.

Standing in the middle of all the daisies was a deer jumping up and down.

"I am so glad you are here," she said. "I have exciting news."

Sofia leaned over to Bella and asked, "What is Debbie Deer feeling?"

Bella answered, "She is excited about something. She is smiling and her voice sounds really happy."

Bella and Sofia ran to Debbie's side to see why she was so excited.

Debbie's high pitched voice yelled out, "I want you to meet my new family. My twin fawns were born yesterday. They are so beautiful. I know that you understand my excitement, Bella. It is now time to learn what to say when you feel empathy about my wonderful news."

Bella sat down in the daisies and listened with eagerness to understand.

"Empathy is showing others kindness and sharing this understanding in an appropriate way," Debbie answered. "If you are excited about my new fawns, you would say kind words."

Bella stood up in the daisies, walked over to Debbie and said, "I am so happy for you. I feel your joy and happiness. Congratulations."

13

Debbie asked Bella to take the star out of her backpack and write the words: **say kind words** at the top.

"I want to learn more Sofia and Debbie," Bella expressed. "We need to keep going."

They walked out of the yellow daisy field and down a new trail. Off in the distance they could hear water running. They looked at each other and together they walked faster.

As they turned the corner, there was a waterfall running over a cliff. The pool of water below was clear and deep. Along the sides of the water were three blue herons shaking with wide open eyes.

With fear in his voice, one of the heron's said, "We are so glad you found the hidden waterfall in the forest. We need help to get out of the water pool." "Our feet are stuck in the mud and we are scared," said Hector Heron.

Bella could see the fear on their faces. She could understand feeling scared because there were times she had felt scared too. She knew that when she understands other's feelings, she needs to do something to show empathy.

Bella walked to the edge of the water. She reached out to Hector Heron, placed both hands around his body and pulled with all her strength. She could feel his body shaking and understood that she needed to act fast.

"It will be okay," she reassured, "I will help you get out of the water."

One by one, Bella pulled and wiggled the three herons out of the water. As each heron stood in the grass, they stopped shaking and said, "Thank you, you are so kind, thank you."

The blue herons told Bella to add to her star the words: **do caring actions.**

Bella stood with pride next to her new friends. "My journey has taught me so much," she said. "I know what empathy is. I understand when you feel empathy you need to say and do something to show you care. I can show empathy to develop new friendships. That is why empathy is so popular."

The three herons flapped their wings with agreement. Together they said, "Yes, Bella, you understand. Your journey is complete. Go back home and share your knowledge with everyone. Make empathy the most popular way to make and keep friends."

Bella hugged Sofia and said, "You taught me that empathy is to understand other's feelings."

She hugged Debbie and added, "you taught me to say kind words. When we arrived at the waterfall, you both watched me show the three herons that I care about them."

The three herons spread their wings in a circle around Bella and shared their appreciation for all the help. "We will never forget you," Hector Heron expressed. "You will always be a very special friend to all of us."

Bella picked up her backpack and looked at her star with the words;

Understand feelings
Say kind words
Do caring actions

She learned that empathy is important to make and to keep friends.

Bella waved goodbye to her friends and started her journey home. She learned so much from them that she ran down the path, through the daisies, around the clover field and over the hills. Her journey to find empathy was complete. Now it was time to practice compassion and care for people.

Each morning Bella would look at the star:
**understand feelings, say kind words and do caring
actions**. Bella would take the time to understand and
feel empathy. She shared these feelings in her words
and actions by caring and helping her classmates.

One day on the school playground, Bella and her friends saw a girl standing alone by the playground equipment. She walked over and could see that she was sad.

"You look sad and I was wondering if we could help you," Bella said. "If you want to play tag with us, come join us. We know what sadness feels like. We want you to be happy and have fun at recess."

Bella helped other classmates to understand empathy, too. They knew what to say and do to show kindness and caring. All the boys and girls showed good character in their words and actions.

Start your journey today.

Being a good friend in school
is the person who understands empathy.

Show you care about the feelings of others.

Say kind words to let people know
you are a nice person.

Do caring actions like playing
together and helping each other.

Your friendships will grow
and your popularity will be noticed
because you chose
a kind and caring journey.

Enjoy the adventure and be a star.

Your Backpack Star

Color and cut out the star and carry it in your backpack.
Write in the middle of the star: ....Understand feelings
Write at the top of the star: ....Say kind words
Write at the bottom of the star: ....Do caring actions

Feeling Empathy from Others

Writing activity

Sometime in our lives, we feel sad about something that happened to us or someone else. We feel great sadness and sometimes cry.

Write about a time that you were sad and someone showed you empathy.

What happened to make you feel sad?

_____

_____

_____

What did they say and do to help you to feel better?

_____

_____

_____

What happened after they showed empathy?

_____

_____

_____

What did you learn about empathy from this experience?

_____

_____

_____

Help Bella Reach the Star

Empathy Maze: Help Bella find the empathy star.

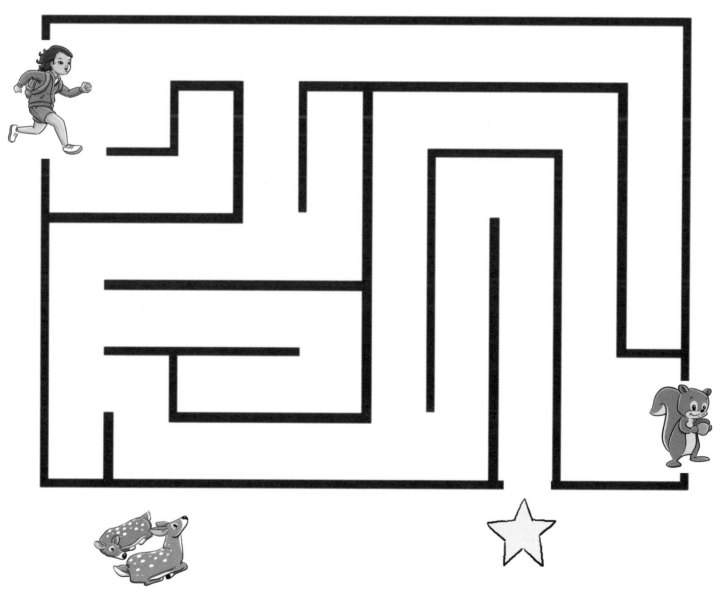

33

Feelings Word Search

Find the following feelings in the word search below:

SAD	FRUSTRATED	FRIGHTENED	AFRAID	PROUD
MAD	EXCITED	NERVOUS	GLAD	THANKFUL
ANGRY	LONELY	JOY	GROUCHY	HURT
HAPPY	SCARED	CONFUSED	WORRIED	

Highlight the Empathy emotions:

EMBARRASSED, GUILTY, RESPONSIBLE, CONCERNED, ASHAMED, CARING

```
H M D W E S W N W X W C I D D Q N P N F
O H E Y M O O S U A L O Q N E N B Q G M
F R U S T R A T E D S N S A S T K D K Q
L U F K N A H T Q C K C U T S I I N Y Y
H A P P Y A P I A D Y E O W A M C C E M
Q A K B H V S R V H L R V J R B X A X F
Z X A V B O E H C W D N R M R G F B D E
J T B T W D P U A L Q E E G A A G P K P
R Y R D Z O O R N M E D N O B T O X Y K
J O D I A R F A O L E Y U I M M D G Q T
T Z D F G D A S B U G D H O E Z M N M A
G S Y V R Y D I W C D U I Y B N T I X U
N P D Z R I S A O D R G Y O T W Z R B J
B R M G V N G N M T Q H W K G L S A C O
O S N L O W F H W O R R I E D L I C X G
F A Q P L U Z V T I O A S X N O E U I L
H X S W S A E T X E G P L K O N N I G A
B E O E T E Y B J I N Z T Y W E I M V D
R D D B A F F Q N O E V O B L V Q V R
J J C Z L F J S W N F F D J H Y Q R P E
```

34

Popularity with Empathy

In a group, make a poster with all the ways to be popular with empathy.
In the middle of the poster write the word: **EMPATHY**.

Write or draw pictures that show empathy. As you work on this poster, talk about why it is more popular to show others empathy than to bully. Discuss in your group how you can help your school make Empathy the most popular way to treat people. Write your ideas in the box below before you work on your poster in your group.

EMPATHY

Activity #6

What are they Feeling? Identify Empathy

In each scenario, what is the feeling that you think describes the best answer?

1. Lena wanted to go to her friend's birthday party, but she is going out of town to visit her Grandma. How is Lena feeling?

2. Josh was racing his classmates during recess and tripped and fell down right before he crossed the finish line. How is Josh feeling?

3. Mrs. Anderson corrected all her third grade student reading tests. Each student scored above 90% on the test. How is Mrs. Anderson feeling?

4. Sofia opened a birthday present and received something she wanted for a long time. How is Sofia feeling?

5. Kevin and his Mom were shopping at the Mall. When Kevin turned around he could not find his Mom. How is Kevin feeling?

6. Casey and his friends found out that the other kickball team cheated during the game. How is Casey feeling?

7. Kelli won the art contest for her watercolor painting of wild animals.
   How is Kelli feeling?

8. Keaton could not find his friends at recess. He sat on the bench by himself.
   How is Keaton feeling?

9. Mr. Potts was talking with another teacher. When he came back into his classroom, his students were out of their seats and talking loudly.
   How is Mr. Potts feeling?

10. You and a friend want to go to a movie. Your Mom said no.
    How are you feeling?

36

© YouthLight, Inc.

Classroom Pledge and Flag?

Write a classroom pledge to make empathy popular at your school.

In this class, we pledge to:

_____

_____

_____

_____

_____

Design a classroom empathy flag:

Brainstorm: How to Make Empathy Popular

In a group, brainstorm all the ways to make empathy popular at your school.

Our ideas to make empathy popular at our school:

1

2

3

4

5

6

7

8

9

Color Activity:
Bella's Adventure

Color the picture: Bella and her animal friends who helped her learn about empathy.

Bella

Drawing Activity:
Show you care!

Draw a picture of you and your friends showing classmates empathy at your school.
Draw the picture to show you and your friends saying kind words or doing caring actions.

Poster for Your Classroom

41

Match the Kind Word Phrase

Read the kind word phrase and circle the correct answer when you say these kind words.

I like you.
(You would say to a friend or say to a stranger)

You're fun to play with.
(You would say to a friend or a say to a chair)

I can help you.
(You would say to a parent or say to a tree)

Thank you.
(You would say to a teacher or say to a dog)

Please.
(You would say to a grandma or say to a bush)

You're welcome.
(You would say to a grandpa or say to a bucket)

Be my friend.
(You would say to a friend or say to an apple)

I care about you.
(You would say to an uncle or say to a book)

I understand how you feel.
(You would say to an aunt or say to a piece of paper)

You can play with us.
(You would say to a classmate or say to a door)

I will share with you.
(You would say to a cousin or say to a cabinet)

Guess What I am Feeling?

Make a list of five feeling words.

1 _____

2 _____

3 _____

4 _____

5 _____

Pantomime an emotion and have your classmates guess what the feeling is.

If they guess correct, circle the feeling in your list and tell them what you would like to say to show you empathy.

When I feel _____ I would like you to say _____.

Ask one of your classmates to practice with you.

Activity #14

My Hero

Write about a person who shows empathy. Tell why this person is a hero and what they said or did to become a hero. Draw a picture of your hero in the box.

Activity #15

Empathy Billboard

When we travel, we see highway billboards that advertise information for all to see. We can learn about many things just by reading the signs along the way as we travel.

Your job is to become an advertising graphic artist. You need to design a billboard about empathy. You can use any of the words or characters that you learned in the book, "Bella: The Empathy Adventure."

About the Author

Sandy Ragona, MSEd, is an elementary school counselor at J.F. Kennedy School in Dubuque, Iowa with over 30 years of experience in school counseling. Sandy has been an adjunct professor at Loras College, Drake University and Morningside College, all in Iowa. She has led numerous workshops and training sessions locally and nationally. She is the author of four books, *Eliminating Bullying, Please Stop I Don't Like That, Coming to School is Really Cool,* and *Becoming Someone's Hero*.

About the Illustrator

Brian Dumm is an illustrator and art educator from central/western Pennsylvania. For more information please visit his webpage; bcdummillustration.com